HEINEMANN GUIDED READERS

INTERMEDIATE LEVEL

PIERS PLOWRIGHT

The Smuggler

HEINEMANN

INTERMEDIATE LEVEL

Series Editor: John Milne

The Heinemann Guided Readers provide a choice of enjoyable reading material for learners of English. The series is published at five levels – Starter, Beginner, Elementary, Intermediate and Upper. At **Intermediate Level**, the control of content and language has the following main features:

Information Control
Information which is vital to the understanding of the story is presented in an easily assimilated manner and is repeated when necessary. Difficult allusion and metaphor are avoided and cultural backgrounds are made explicit.

Structure Control
Most of the structures used in the Readers will be familiar to students who have completed an elementary course of English. Other grammatical features may occur, but their use is made clear through context and reinforcement. This ensures that the reading, as well as being enjoyable, provides a continual learning situation for the students. Sentences are limited in most cases to a maximum of three clauses and within sentences there is a balanced use of adverbial and adjectival phrases. Great care is taken with pronoun reference.

Vocabulary Control
There is a basic vocabulary of approximately 1,600 words. Help is given to the students in the form of illustrations, which are closely related to the text.

Glossary
Some difficult words and phrases in this book are important for understanding the story. Some of these words are explained in the story, some are shown in the pictures, and others are marked with a number like this . . .[3] Words with a number are explained in the Glossary on page 77.

Contents

A Note About This Story

When you drive from one country to another, you have to cross a frontier. The frontier is the place where two countries meet.

At the frontier you have to show your passport and go through customs. There are many things which you cannot take from one country to another without paying money. The people who work in customs are called customs officers. Their job is to stop people taking things into their country without paying money. The customs officers ask you, 'Have you anything to declare?' And then you must tell them if you have anything for which you should pay money.

Some people try to take things across frontiers without paying money. Such people are called smugglers. A smuggler can make a lot of money by smuggling things into another country and selling them there.

The People In This Story

In this story you will meet:

Harker's Gang[1]
Harker
Fame
Zara
Don

Ezra's Gang
Ezra
Guido
Robert
Skull

Customs Officers
Rank and Silver

Police
Inspector Roland

The Places In This Story

GOLA RIVER

DON'S HIDE-OUT

GOLA BRIDGE

QUARRY

MOUNTAINS

DARNA

LAKE DARNA

AMBUSH POINT

HARKER'S HUT

FRONTIER POST

CUSTOMS SHED

1

A Man in a Hurry

Emil Harker was a rich man. But this particular Tuesday evening, he was a worried man. He was more worried than he had ever been in his life. Harker was sitting at a desk in his office. His office was in a small forest hut.

Harker sat at his desk and looked at the piece of paper in front of him. There was something written on the piece of paper – a short poem.

Harker had written the poem himself. It was not a very good poem, but then Harker was not a poet, and he had written the poem in a hurry. He hadn't got much time left.

About an hour earlier, the phone had rung in the hut. Harker had answered it.

'Harker?' said a voice. Harker recognised the voice.

'Ezra,' said Harker. 'What do you want?'

'Where is it?' asked Ezra.

'Where is what?' asked Harker.

'You know,' said Ezra.

'I *don't* know,' said Harker.

'Stop playing games,' said Ezra.

'I'm not playing games,' said Harker.

'Oh yes you are,' said the voice. 'I'm coming to see you.'

'Now look,' began Harker. But Ezra had put the phone down.

It was then that Harker wrote the poem. He sat at his desk and wrote fast. He tore up two or three pieces of paper before he was satisfied. At last the poem was finished. Harker folded the paper and wrote across the front:

To John Samuel Fame – please read carefully.

Harker put his pen in his pocket and looked at his watch. It was half past nine.

Without warning, the hut door opened. A tall man with a pale face and a moustache stood in the doorway. Behind him were two other men who carried guns.

Harker stood up. 'Now just a minute Ezra,' he said, 'Let's talk.'

'You're the one who's going to talk,' said Ezra. 'Where is it?'

'I've told you,' said Harker, 'I don't know what you're talking about.'

'Hold his arms,' shouted Ezra to the two men. The men moved fast across the room and got hold of Harker. Ezra walked over to the desk. He saw the folded piece of paper and picked it up. He looked at it, then unfolded it and read the poem.

'What's this?' he said.

Harker said nothing. He was sweating[2].

8

2

At the Frontier

Harker wasn't the only person who had an important phone call that Tuesday evening. At ten o'clock, the phone rang in the customs shed at the frontier. The phone rang three times and then one of the two customs officers in the shed answered it.

'Hello. Frontier Customs here,' he said.

'Hello,' said a voice, 'Inspector Roland here.'

'Hello, Inspector,' said the customs officer, 'what can I do for you?'

'Do you know a man called John Samuel Fame?' asked the Inspector.

'Yes,' said the customs officer, 'he crosses the frontier a lot. Perhaps two or three times a week. He's a businessman.'

'That's what he says,' said the Inspector.

'Do you know him?' said the customs officer.

'Very well,' said the Inspector.

'What do you want me to do about him?' asked the customs officer.

'Watch him,' said the Inspector. 'Search his car.'

The customs officer, whose name was Silver, put down the phone. Silver was a thin man with a high forehead and large ears. He crossed the room and sat down on a chair by the window.

'Who was that?' asked Rank, the other customs officer.

Rank was a much fatter man than Silver, with a small moustache.

'Inspector Roland,' said Silver.

'What did he want?' asked Rank. Rank was sitting on a chair with his legs up on a table, reading a newspaper.

'He asked me about John Samuel Fame,' said Silver.

'Who?' asked Rank.

'John Samuel Fame,' repeated Silver, 'the businessman who crosses the frontier two or three times a week. He always drives a smart grey car.'

'Oh yes,' said Rank. 'What about him?'

'Inspector Roland told us to watch him,' said Silver, 'and search his car.'

'Why?' asked Rank.

'The Inspector didn't say,' said Silver.

'Oh,' said Rank, and turned over a page of his newspaper.

Silver opened a large exercise book that was lying on the wooden table in front of him and began to write in it.

A fly landed on Rank's head and crawled down his forehead and nose. Rank brushed it off and went on reading the newspaper. The clock on the wall behind him ticked loudly and the fly crawled across the lightshade over his head.

Just then both customs officers heard a car. Silver looked up and stopped writing, and the guard outside moved out into the middle of the road. The car came round the corner and stopped beside the guard. The guard told the driver to get out. The driver switched off the engine and the headlights, got out, and followed the guard up the wooden steps of the customs hut. The guard opened the door for him and the man went inside.

Silver, the thin customs officer, looked up. John Samuel Fame was standing in front of him. Fame was wearing a smart dark suit and an open-necked shirt. He was a tall thin man – and rather good-looking.

'It's me again,' said John Samuel Fame.

'Your passport, please,' said Silver without smiling.

Fame gave his passport to Silver. Silver opened it and turned

over the pages, while Rank went on reading the newspaper. Fame
stood the other side of the table and waited.

'Are you John Samuel Fame?' asked Silver.

'Yes, you know I am,' said Fame smiling.

'And are you a businessman?' asked Silver.

'Yes, of course!' said Fame.

'Why are you crossing the frontier?' asked Silver.

'On business, as usual,' said Fame.

'How long are you going to stay here?' asked Silver.

'Two days, as usual,' said Fame. 'What *is* all this . . .?'

'Have you anything to declare?' asked Silver.

'Nothing,' said Fame.

'Have you got any luggage?' asked Silver.

'One suitcase,' said Fame.

Silver turned to the fat customs officer.

'Go and have a look in his car,' he said.

Rank nodded, folded the newspaper, and went outside. Fame followed him.

'Where's the case?' asked Rank.

'In the boot³,' said Fame.

'Let's have a look,' said Rank.

Fame opened the boot and pulled out the case.

'Open the case,' said Rank.

Fame opened it. Rank put his fat hands inside the case and felt among the clothes. He pulled out a thick brown bottle.

'What's this?' he asked Fame.

'Medicine,' said Fame, and laughed.

'Hm,' said Rank, and put the bottle back.

Then Rank looked inside the car, and under the car and on the roof. Fame stood and watched him. Rank found nothing.

'Follow me,' Rank said to Fame, and the two men went back into the customs shed.

'He hasn't got anything,' said Rank to Silver.

'Right, Mr Fame,' said Silver. 'You can go. Goodnight.'

'Goodnight,' said Fame. He went out and shut the door, walked down the steps, and over to his car. He got in and shut the door. The guard walked over to the pole across the road, and lifted it up. Fame started the car and drove off. The guard lowered the pole and watched Fame's car disappearing into the distance. Inside the customs hut, Rank, the fat customs officer, picked up his newspaper again and went on reading.

3

Strange Meeting

John Samuel Fame drove very fast along the white road. There was a full moon and there were no clouds so he could see clearly, even without the headlights. The road was straight and flat and empty.

Fame looked at his watch. The time was half past ten and Harker had told him to be there at ten o'clock. Fame realised he was already half an hour late for his appointment[4]. He knew that Harker would be angry with him, because Harker didn't like people who were late for appointments. John Samuel Fame accelerated[5] and the car roared forward[6] down the white road.

After about ten minutes, Fame saw the turning to Harker's hut. Fame turned left and drove up a hill.

'When you get to the top,' Harker had said, 'stop the car on the edge of the wood and walk until you reach the hut.' Fame stopped the car and walked into the wood.

In the moonlight it was easy to see his way, and he walked quietly between the trees. After about three minutes he saw the hut. There was a light on inside and Fame saw Harker's car parked outside.

'When you get to the hut,' Harker had said, 'whistle three times and wait for an answer.' Fame whistled, once, twice, three times, and waited.

There was no answer. He whistled again. There was still no answer. Where was Harker? What was wrong? Fame whistled again. Still no answer. Something was wrong.

Fame carefully walked towards the hut. Silently, he reached the door. It was half open. Fame pushed the door right open and went inside. There was no one there.

In the middle of the room was a chair and a desk with a lamp on it. There were some books and papers on the desk too. In one corner of the room was a small black cupboard. The cupboard door was open and there were some cups and glasses inside. On one wall there was a photograph of a young man on a horse. Next to the photograph there was a large map.

Fame crossed over to the desk. A green pen and a small notebook were on the desk, among the books and papers. Fame recognised them. They belonged to Harker, but where *was* Harker? Fame was three-quarters of an hour late, so perhaps Harker had gone. But Harker's car was still there and his pen and his notebook were still on the desk.

Suddenly Fame noticed the shadow[7]. It was moving backwards and forwards across the opposite wall. Fame looked up. Hanging from the ceiling of the hut, just to the left of the door, was a man. He was swinging from the end of a rope. It was Harker.

4

A Narrow Escape

Fame stood still, looking at the swinging man. Below him a chair lay on its side on the floor. So, thought Fame, Harker had stood on the chair, tied the rope to the roof, tightened the rope around his neck and jumped. Fame picked the chair up, put it underneath the swinging man, and climbed up on it. He put out his hands and felt Harker's body. Harker was still warm – he hadn't been dead long.

Fame took a small knife out of one of his coat pockets and putting one arm round Harker's body, cut the rope. Harker was a heavy man and Fame couldn't hold him. Harker, Fame, and the chair fell to the floor.

Fame got up and looked at Harker. Then he knelt down and loosened the rope round Harker's neck. Then Fame saw some blood on Harker's shirt. He lifted up the shirt and looked underneath. There wasn't a mark on Harker's body. The blood on Harker's shirt wasn't Harker's blood. Someone had been in that room before Fame. Someone had fought with Harker.

Fame looked round the room. Fame noticed a broken bottle on the floor near the door, which he hadn't seen before. The bottle had broken into three pieces and the three pieces lay on the floor near the door. Someone *had* attacked Harker. Harker hadn't hanged himself. Some men had been in the hut before Fame. They had fought with Harker, and then they had hanged him.

Fame began to look through Harker's pockets but they were empty. Someone had already gone through Harker's pockets and taken everything. Fame looked round the room again. Then he saw the bit of paper lying on the floor, near Harker's desk. Fame picked it up. There was writing on the paper – Harker's writing. Fame looked at the writing but he could not understand it. It was a poem.

So Harker had written a poem. But why? Harker wasn't a poet. He didn't even read poetry. Harker was a clever man, a tough man, but he was interested in money, not in poetry. He read newspapers, he didn't read poetry.

Fame was about to put the poem in his pocket, when he saw what was written on the front:

To John Samuel Fame – please read carefully.

So it was a message – a message for him. Fame read the poem carefully but he still did not understand it.

GREAT MEN
DO NOT WALK EASY ROADS.
TALL MEN
STRAIN UNDER HEAVY LOADS.
THEY BEND BENEATH THE WEIGHT,
GET TIRED BENEATH THE LOAD.
THEY GO IN PAIN AND HATE
THEY WANDER DOWN THAT ROAD,
BUT THEN AGAINST THE WALL THEY STAND
AND NEAR ONE ROCK THEY REST THEIR
HAND.
EMIL HARKER.

Just as Fame was finishing the poem, he heard voices. Men's voices. The men were coming towards the door.

Fame just had time to get to the window, raise it silently and get through before the men reached the hut. He landed on his feet and leant against the outside wall of the hut. He listened. He could hear the two voices, one deep and strong, the other high and nervous, with an Italian accent.

'Someone's been here,' said the man with the high voice. 'Someone's been here and cut him down.'

'Where's the piece of paper with the poem on it?' said the other man, with the deep voice.

'I don't know,' said the first man. 'I can't see it. I'm sure I must have dropped it on the floor.'

There was silence for a moment. 'It's not here,' said the man with the high voice.

'Someone's been here and taken it,' said the man with the deep voice.

'The window!' shouted one of the men suddenly.

Fame didn't wait. He ran through the trees and towards his car. When he reached the car, he took the keys out of his coat pocket. Behind him, Fame could hear the shouts of the two men running from the hut. Fame unlocked the car door, jumped in and started the car.

As the car roared away down the hill in the moonlight, Fame heard the sound of guns.

5

A Night in Darna

Fame didn't stop until he reached the town of Darna. It was after midnight when he stopped the car outside the Garden Hotel. Fame always stayed at the Garden Hotel when he went to Darna.

There was a light on in the hotel entrance but the door was shut. Fame rang the bell and waited. After a minute the door was opened a little and an old man put his head round.

It was the night porter at the Garden Hotel. He'd worked there for years.

'Hello, Mr Fame,' said the porter smiling. 'You're late.'

'Yes,' said Fame, 'I had a bad journey.'

'Oh, I'm sorry,' said the porter. 'But your room's ready.'

'Good,' said Fame, 'I'm tired.'

The porter took Fame's case and led Fame into the hotel. Fame's room was number 18 on the first floor. Fame had stayed there before. It was a nice room with a view over the lake. But tonight Fame wasn't interested in the view. When the porter left him, Fame sat in a chair by the window, thinking.

Harker was dead. That was certain. And Harker had been murdered. That, too, was certain. He had probably been murdered by the two men at the hut. They had killed him and then hung his body from the ceiling. They had wanted people to think Harker had killed himself. But Fame knew better.

Why had they killed him? And why had they returned to search for that piece of paper? The piece of paper was addressed to him. Fame took it out of his pocket, unfolded it and read the poem again:

```
GREAT MEN
DO NOT WALK EASY ROADS.
TALL MEN
STRAIN UNDER HEAVY LOADS.
THEY BEND. BENEATH THE WEIGHT,
GET TIRED BENEATH THE LOAD.
THEY GO IN PAIN AND HATE
THEY WANDER DOWN THAT ROAD,
BUT THEN AGAINST THE WALL THEY STAND
AND NEAR ONE ROCK THEY REST THEIR
                         HAND.
            EMIL HARKER.
```

What *was* the message hidden in this strange poem? Harker wanted Fame to understand the message but he didn't want the other men to understand it.

Fame tried to think about Harker. Harker was rich, he was a smuggler, he was powerful, and he was Fame's boss[8]. Harker had many enemies. Probably he had many secrets. Now he was dead – murdered. What was Fame to do?

He couldn't go to the police. The police were no friends of Harker's or Fame's. He couldn't go back across the frontier, not yet. Fame had a job to do. He decided to ring Zara.

There was a telephone on a small white table next to the bed. Fame rang Zara's number and waited.

'Hello,' said Zara.

'Zara?' said Fame.

'Who's that?' said the voice.

'It's me,' said Fame, 'Fame.'

'Fame,' said the voice. 'What are you ringing at this time for?'

'I'm sorry, Zara,' said Fame, 'but I've got to see you very soon. Harker's dead.'

'Dead!' said Zara. She sounded shocked.

'Yes,' said Fame. 'Look, can you come over here first thing in the morning? I'm at the Garden Hotel. I'll meet you on the terrace at half past eight. OK?'

'OK,' said Zara, 'see you then.'

'Goodbye,' said Fame, and he put the phone down.

Fame undressed and got into bed. Next to the bed on the small white table was a radio. Fame turned on the radio to listen to the news. *'The golden head of the Pharaoh Chefren IV, which was stolen from the Darna Municipal Museum yesterday evening, is still missing. The police under Inspector Francis Roland are still looking for the head.'*

Fame smiled. He hadn't heard about the stolen head, but he knew Inspector Roland. Fame turned off the radio and was asleep within a few minutes.

6

On the Terrace

The next morning Fame was awake early. The first thing he did was to make a copy of the poem and then he went downstairs. It was getting light and people were beginning to move in the streets. Fame went out onto the terrace.

Zara arrived an hour later. She was looking very pretty in a light blue dress and a dark blue headscarf.

'Hello, Zara,' said Fame.

'Hello, Fame,' said Zara.

'Sit down,' said Fame.

When they had both sat down, Fame called the waiter and ordered two coffees.

'Well,' said Zara, 'so Harker's dead.'

'Yes,' said Fame. And he told her what had happened. He told Zara how he had found Harker hanging, how the two men had then arrived and looked for the piece of paper, how he had escaped and spent the night at the hotel.

'And where's the poem?' said Zara, when Fame had finished.

'Here,' said Fame. He handed her the piece of paper and Zara read the poem.

'There's a message hidden in the poem,' said Zara.

'I know there is,' said Fame, 'but what *is* the message?'

'I don't know,' said Zara, 'but we can find out.'

'It'll take time,' said Fame. 'And before we try and find out the answer, what are we going to do next, now that Harker's dead?'

'Well,' said Zara, 'the business can go on. Don's waiting for you and the car in the hide-out[9] as usual.'

'Yes, but who'll be the boss now that Harker's dead?' asked Fame. 'Ezra?'

'Not Ezra,' said Zara. 'That's something I was going to tell you. Ezra and Harker had an argument last week and Ezra left the gang. He's working on his own now.'

'I see,' said Fame. 'Who's in charge then?'

'I am,' said Zara, smiling.

'You?' said Fame.

'Yes,' said Zara, 'why not? Or don't you think a woman *can* lead a gang?'

'Well,' said Fame, 'I don't know . . .'

'Anyway,' said Zara, 'I'm the new boss, so I give the orders. And I want you to keep your appointment with Don this morning. Where's the car?'

'Outside,' said Fame.

Just then the waiter came back with the two coffees and put them down on the table. Fame paid the waiter and he went away.

'Why did Harker and Ezra quarrel?' asked Fame.

'Ezra never liked Harker,' said Zara, 'and then last week they argued over a job[10].'

'What job?' asked Fame.

'I don't know,' said Zara, 'but I think it was something important. Ezra shouted at Harker and Harker told him to get out.'

'I see,' said Fame. He was quiet for a moment. 'You don't think,' Fame asked suddenly, 'that Ezra might have killed Harker, do you?'

'I don't know,' replied Zara. 'It's possible.'

Fame and Zara were the only two people on the terrace. It was already quite hot and most people were indoors, eating their breakfast in the shade.

Then another waiter came out of the hotel and came up to Fame. The other waiter was a bald-headed man with a scar on his left cheek.

'Telephone call for you, Mr Fame,' he said.

'Thanks,' said Fame. 'Excuse me a minute, Zara.'

'Of course,' said Zara. 'I'll wait here.'

21

Fame crossed the terrace and went into the hotel. The phone was lying on the desk in the hall. Fame picked it up.

'Hello,' he said. No answer.

'Hello?' said Fame again. Still no answer.

'Hello, who is it?' asked Fame.

Then he heard the phone put down on the other end. What *was* going on? Fame put his phone down and went back onto the terrace. Zara wasn't there, nor was the bald-headed waiter. Fame began to sweat.

'Waiter!' shouted Fame. 'Waiter!'

The waiter who had brought the coffee came out of the hotel. 'Yes sir?' he said.

'Where's the other waiter?' asked Fame.

'What do you mean?' said the waiter. 'I'm the only waiter on duty at the moment.'

'A bald man,' said Fame, 'with a scar on his left cheek.'

'A bald man with a scar,' said the waiter. 'We haven't got a waiter who looks like that, sir.'

Fame didn't wait to hear any more. A car was starting up on the other side of the garden wall. Fame ran to the edge of the terrace, jumped over the wall and down onto the pavement below. A long black American car was pulling away from the pavement and Fame could see the driver. It was the bald-headed waiter.

7

Keeping an Appointment

Fame ran across the street and jumped into his own car. He started the engine and accelerated away from the pavement. The American car was turning into the main road that went out of the town and into the hills. Fame followed it.

As long as they were in the town, Fame kept close to the American car. But when the two cars had left the town and were on the hill road, the American car moved further ahead. Fame could just read the car number, ZX 425. He wrote it with his finger on the dust of the window.

Then after another minute, Fame could no longer see the American car, but he kept going. He was driving in the hills above Darna, looking down over the town and the lake. Fame knew the road well. He took it each time he came to Darna. The road to Don's hide-out turned off this road a few miles ahead.

Well, Zara had told him to go and see Don, and at least he would get help there. Don was a member of their gang. Fame drove on as fast as he could. He was just coming round a long left hand bend when he saw a girl in a blue dress standing at the side of the road and waving at him. It was Zara. Fame put on the brakes and the car stopped.

'Get in!' he shouted.

Zara got in. She looked pale and worried and her right cheek was bleeding.

'Are you all right?' said Fame.

'Yes,' said Zara, 'but he's got the poem.'

'Don't worry,' said Fame, 'I've got a copy of the poem. What happened?'

'Well,' said Zara, 'as soon as you'd gone in to answer the phone, the bald-headed waiter came over to our table. I thought he was going to take my coffee cup. But he suddenly held me tightly and put his hand over my mouth. I tried to escape but he was very strong and had a gun. In the car he took the poem from me and then he left me on the side of the road.'

'Well,' said Fame. 'I've got the car number.'

'And he's got the poem,' said Zara.

'Don't worry,' said Fame, 'I've got a copy.'

'Oh yes,' said Zara, 'I forgot.'

She looked at him.

'Where are we going now?' she asked.

'We're going to Don's,' said Fame. 'We're going to keep that appointment.'

Fame and Zara drove slowly up the road until they came to the turning to Don's hide-out. The sun was now high in the sky and the day was very hot. Fame turned the car into the narrow dusty road. Then the road went down to a small valley and crossed a dried-up stream. Three or four goats were trying to reach the few dusty leaves of an old white tree. Fame sounded his horn[11] twice so that Don would know Fame had arrived. Then he turned in at

24

an open gate.

They were in a small yard. To the left was a long brown shed. To the right was a small flat-roofed house. Some chickens ran across the yard and behind the shed. A fat man with a short black beard and a blue apron came out of the shed as Fame stopped the car.

'Hello, Don,' said Fame.

'Hello, Fame,' said Don, and seeing Zara, he added, 'Hello, Zara.'

'Hello,' said Zara.

'We've got a lot to talk about, Don,' said Fame.

'Go in and sit down,' said Don. 'I'll follow you.'

He spoke slowly and smiled. When he smiled, he showed a row of shining white teeth.

Fame and Zara got out of the car and went into the house. Don drove the car into the shed.

Inside the house it was dark and cool. The shutters were closed and there was a large wooden table in the middle of the room. There was a rocking-chair in one corner and several stools. Zara sat down in the rocking-chair and Fame sat down on one of the stools.

Don came in from the yard and joined them. He gave Fame his car keys and he sat down on a stool. He took a cigar and a box of matches from his apron pocket. He put the cigar in his mouth, struck a match and lit the cigar.

'Well,' he said, sending a cloud of smoke up to the ceiling, 'what's the news?'

'Harker's dead,' said Fame.

Don nearly dropped his cigar. He opened his mouth to speak, but before he could speak, two cars came roaring into the yard. Some men dressed in black jumped out of the cars and ran towards the house. They were policemen. The leading man was not dressed in black. Fame recognised him. It was Inspector Roland.

A fat man with a short black beard and a blue apron came
out of the shed as Fame stopped the car.

8

Inspector Roland

'Well, well,' said Inspector Roland, coming into the room. 'Mr Fame.'

'Hello, Inspector,' said Fame, 'what can we do for you?'

'You can stay where you are,' said the Inspector.

There were four policemen with the Inspector and one of them was a very tall man. He was holding a large gun. He stood by the door and kept the gun pointing at Fame, Zara, and Don.

'Excuse me, Inspector,' said Don, 'but this *is* my house.'

'Shut up,' said Inspector Roland.

The other three policemen began to search the place. One of them crossed the yard to the shed, one of them walked round the yard, and the other began searching Don's house. The tall man stayed by the door pointing the large gun.

A clock on the wall above the rocking-chair ticked loudly. Fame looked at Zara, Zara looked at Fame. They both looked at Don. All three looked at the Inspector and the man with the gun. Nobody said anything. Everything was silent in the house, except for the clock.

After a few minutes, Fame spoke to the Inspector.

'What are they looking for?' he asked.

No answer.

'What are they looking for, Inspector?' Fame asked again.

'Shut up,' said the Inspector.

'All right,' said Fame and he was silent.

For half an hour they sat in the cool room. Zara looked straight ahead of her. Don finished one cigar and lit another one, and Fame tapped his fingers on the wooden table.

'Don't do that!' said the Inspector suddenly.

'Don't do what?' asked Fame.

'Don't tap your fingers on the table,' said the Inspector.

'Sorry,' said Fame and stopped tapping.

Just then one of the men came in from the yard.

'Inspector!' shouted the policeman 'There are two cars in the shed,' said the man. 'Shall I search them?'

'I'll search them myself,' said the Inspector and he went out with the man.

Fame looked at Don and raised his eyebrows. Don shook his head. The very tall policeman with the gun looked suspiciously[12] from Don to Fame, and his finger tightened on the gun. Don smoked his cigar and looked straight ahead of him, while Fame looked at the ceiling. Zara just smiled.

'What are you smiling at?' said Fame to Zara.

'Nothing,' said Zara.

'Nothing?' asked Fame.

'I was thinking,' said Zara.

'What about?' asked Fame.

'Life,' said Zara smiling.

Nobody talked or moved again until Inspector Roland came back a few minutes later.

'The boot of one of the cars is locked,' said the Inspector. 'Who's got the key?'

'I have,' said Fame.

'Give it to me,' said the Inspector.

Fame gave him the key and the Inspector went outside again.

In a few minutes he was back. He called the other three policemen and they all hurried into the room.

The Inspector and all the policemen stood and looked at Don, Fame and Zara. Suddenly the Inspector walked across the room and hit Fame across the face.

'Now,' said the Inspector, 'let's talk.'

9

The Photograph

'What did you do that for?' asked Fame.

The Inspector smiled.

'I just wanted to wake you up,' he said.

'I was awake already,' said Fame.

The Inspector stopped smiling.

'I'm not here to waste my time,' said Inspector Roland. 'I'm looking for something.'

'We noticed that,' said Don.

'You know what I'm looking for, don't you?' said the Inspector, turning to Don.

'No, I don't,' said Don.

'Don't lie to me,' said the Inspector.

'I'm not lying,' said Don. 'What *are* you looking for?'

The Inspector looked hard at Don. Then he turned to one of the policemen.

'Have you got the newspaper?' asked Inspector Roland.

'Here it is, Inspector,' answered the policeman, taking a newspaper from his pocket and handing it to the Inspector.

'Yesterday's paper,' said the Inspector. 'Listen.'

And the Inspector began to read:

Famous Treasure Stolen From Museum

DARNA, Tuesday. — Late yesterday, it was discovered that the museum's most valuable treasure, a 3,000 year old Egyptian gold head of the Pharoah Chefren IV, was missing. The Director of the Museum, Professor K. Tan, said he had no idea how the head was stolen. The head, which is the museum's newest treasure, only arrived there last week. The Darna Police under Inspector Francis Roland are investigating the crime.

29

The Inspector stopped reading and looked up.

'I heard about that,' said Fame.

'When?' asked the Inspector sharply.

'Yesterday evening,' said Fame, 'on the radio.'

He smiled. So did Zara. Don laughed. The Inspector looked annoyed.

'Don't waste my time,' said the Inspector. 'What do you know about the head?'

'Nothing,' said Fame. 'Is that what you're looking for?'

'Perhaps,' said the Inspector. Fame laughed.

'Look, Inspector,' he said, 'I didn't steal that head. Nor did he.' He pointed at Don. 'Nor did she.' He pointed at Zara.

'None of us stole it. You're wasting your time.'

'I'm not so sure,' said the Inspector. 'Look at this.'

He handed Fame a photograph. Fame looked at it. The photograph had been taken inside the museum. It showed a group of men standing round the golden head of Chefren IV. The men were all holding glasses and smiling.

'A lot of important people came to the museum last week,' said the Inspector. 'There was a reception[13] to celebrate the arrival of the Pharaoh's head. That photograph was taken at the reception.'

'I see,' said Fame.

'Now look very closely at the men in the photograph,' said Inspector Roland.

Fame looked – a group of happy smiling men at a party. Fame didn't recognise any of the men at first. Then he looked more closely. There was a man on the left, half hidden by the man in front. It was Harker.

'Do you recognise anybody?' asked the Inspector.

'Yes,' said Fame.

'Who?' asked the Inspector.

'The man on the left,' said Fame. 'It's Harker.'

'Exactly,' said Inspector Roland, 'Harker.'

'OK,' said Fame, 'so Harker was at the reception. What does that prove?'

'Look at the back of the photograph,' said the Inspector.

Fame looked. On the back of the photograph was written:

C 304 MONDAY

It was Harker's writing.

'Do you recognise the writing?' asked the Inspector.

'No,' said Fame.

'Don't you?' said the Inspector. 'Well I'll tell you whose writing it is. It's Harker's.'

'How do you know?' asked Fame.

'We found the photograph in Harker's house,' said Inspector Roland. 'And we are sure that the writing on the back of the photograph is Harker's writing.'

'What were you doing in his house?' asked Fame.

'Searching it,' said the Inspector.

'Why?' asked Fame.

'We had a phone call,' said the Inspector. 'Someone told us to go to Harker's house. They said we'd find something interesting.'

Fame was thinking fast. So Harker had stolen the golden head, or arranged for someone to steal it. Someone had told Inspector Roland. Someone who didn't like Harker. Now Inspector Roland suspected Fame, Don and Zara because they all worked for Harker. But did the Inspector know that Harker was dead?

'Have you got Harker?' Fame asked the Inspector suddenly.

'Not yet,' said Inspector Roland, 'but we'll get him soon. Anyway we've got you.'

So the Inspector didn't know that Harker was dead. Good,

thought Fame. He had an idea.

'Inspector Roland.' Fame said. 'You're quite right. You've got us. But *we* don't know anything about the head. Harker planned this on his own.'

Inspector Roland looked at Fame, then at Don, then at Zara.

'It's quite true, Inspector,' said Zara, 'we know nothing about this business.'

'In fact,' said Fame, 'Harker should have told us about the head, but he didn't. We don't like that. I'm going to suggest an arrangement with you.'

'What kind of arrangement?' asked Inspector Roland.

'You let us go,' said Fame, 'and we'll get Harker for you.'

Inspector Roland laughed and so did the policemen.

'I can't do that,' said the Inspector. 'If I let you go, you'll leave the country tonight with Harker and the head.'

'Look,' said Fame, 'I'll tell you what I'll do. Don here, can stay with you, as a hostage[14]. Let me and Zara go and we'll get Harker for you.'

There was silence in the room. Inspector Roland was thinking. Use a thief to catch a thief, thought the Inspector. Not a bad idea. Fame and Zara would get Harker for him, and then he, Inspector Roland, could get Harker *and* Fame *and* Zara. Not a bad idea at all.

'OK,' said Inspector Roland.

10

Room 304

Inspector Roland accepted the arrangement and his men took Don back to the town. Fame and Zara took one of the two cars from Don's shed. Now they were driving back along the hill road towards Darna.

'Hungry?' Fame asked Zara, as they began to drive down to the town.

'Yes,' said Zara.

'Right,' said Fame. 'I know somewhere nice where we can eat.'

They could see the lake now. The early afternoon sun was shining on the little boats.

Near the bottom of the hill, Fame turned the car off the main road and drove towards the lake. By the lake there was a little restaurant. The restaurant had a garden beside the lake, and there were tables and chairs in the garden. People were eating their lunch at the tables. Fame turned the car into the little car-park by the entrance and stopped.

'Come on, Zara,' he said. 'Let's go.'

But Zara didn't move. She was staring at the car parked next to them.

'What is it?' asked Fame.

'Look at the number,' said Zara.

Fame looked. ZX 425. Of course! It was the car in which Zara had been taken away earlier that day.

'What shall we do?' asked Zara.

'Go and eat,' said Fame. 'We're both hungry.'

'What about our bald-headed friend?' asked Zara.

'He won't dare do anything in public,' said Fame. 'Come on.'

33

So they both went into the garden and sat down at a table by the edge of the lake and ordered a meal.

'Can you see him?' asked Fame, as they were eating.

'Who?' asked Zara.

'Our bald-headed friend,' said Fame.

'No,' said Zara, 'he must be inside.'

Both Zara and Fame were very hungry and they ate a lot.

'Well, what are we going to do next?' asked Fame, as they were drinking coffee.

'You tell me,' said Zara.

'I thought you were the boss,' said Fame.

'I am,' said Zara, smiling, 'but this is *your* plan.'

'OK,' said Fame. 'Do you remember what was written on the back of that photograph?'

'A letter and a number and a day,' said Zara. 'C . . .'

'C 304 Monday,' said Fame.

'What does that mean?' asked Zara.

'Well, first of all,' said Fame, 'what happened on Monday?'

'Lots of things,' said Zara.

'One *particular* thing happened,' said Fame. 'Think.'

Zara thought. 'Oh yes,' she said, 'the golden head was stolen.'

'Exactly,' said Fame. 'And the golden head is supposed to be the head of the Pharaoh Chef . . .'

'C for Chefren,' said Zara excitedly.

'Exactly,' said Fame again. 'The golden head of the Pharaoh which was stolen.'

'But what about 304?' asked Zara.

'I'm not sure,' said Fame, 'but I can guess.'

'What's your guess?' asked Zara.

'I think it's a room number,' said Fame. 'A room number in a hotel and I only know *one* hotel which has so many rooms.'

'Which hotel is that?' asked Zara.

'The Imperial Hotel,' replied Fame.

'Ssh!' said Zara suddenly. She was looking past Fame towards the restaurant building. Fame turned and looked too. The bald-headed 'waiter' was coming out into the garden with two other men. One of the men was tall and dark and dressed in a white suit. He looked Italian. The other man was much shorter and rather fat. They didn't notice Fame and Zara, but went and sat down at another table, half hidden by a tree.

'They didn't see us,' said Zara.

'But we saw them,' said Fame, 'and we can watch them closely from here. Another cup of coffee?'

'Yes please,' said Zara.

And Fame poured Zara another cup of coffee.

'Shall we go to the Imperial Hotel?' asked Zara after a few minutes.

'Yes,' said Fame, 'but there's no hurry. I'd like to watch those three men over there and see what they do.'

So Zara and Fame sat in the afternoon sun by the side of the lake drinking their coffee and watching the three men.

Zara suddenly turned to Fame and touched his arm. The bald man and his two friends had finished their lunch and were crossing the garden towards the car-park. Fame made a sign to Zara to sit still. They both watched the three men get into their car and drive slowly off. Fame paid the bill and he and Zara got into their car.

They followed the other car into Darna. When the car reached the town, it turned into the market and followed the narrow streets down to the main square – Parliament Square. In Parliament Square, the car turned right and followed a wide street towards the richer part of town.

This part of town was called The Park, because of the large public park in the middle of it. Along one side of the park, there was an avenue. The avenue was full of hotels, and the largest of the hotels was The Imperial. The car with the three men in it stopped outside The Imperial. Fame stopped a little way behind them, in the shade of some trees.

'Well,' he said to Zara, 'that's interesting. The Imperial Hotel.'

'Are you going in?' asked Zara.

'Of course,' said Fame, 'but I want you to stay here.'

'Why?' asked Zara.

'In case anything happens,' said Fame.

'OK,' said Zara. 'Good luck.'

'Thanks,' said Fame and went into the hotel.

He went straight up to the reception desk.

'Is the gentleman in Room 304 in?' he asked the porter.

The porter looked at the rows of keys behind him.

'No sir,' he said, 'not yet. But his friends have just arrived. They are all up in Room 303, if you want to go and join them.'

Fame hesitated. So the bald-headed man and his two friends were staying in Room 303, next to Room 304. Who was staying in Room 304? Fame decided to wait.

'No,' said Fame, 'I'll wait here.'

Fame went and sat in the far corner of the foyer, just behind a pillar. From here he could see everyone who came in without being seen.

He had been waiting for about five minutes, when a tall man with a fat pale face and moustache came in. Fame knew him immediately. It was Ezra. Ezra went up to the desk. The porter said something and pointed in Fame's direction. Fame turned and walked fast out of the foyer and into the coffee lounge. He knew the hotel well. At the end of the coffee lounge were some stairs which led down to a side door; on the other side of the door was the street.

'Well,' said Zara as Fame climbed into the car beside her, 'you weren't long. Did you find out anything?'

'Yes,' said Fame, 'the man staying in Room 304 is Ezra.'

11

Return Journey

At ten o'clock the next morning, Fame was driving towards the frontier. He had left Zara in Darna. Whatever else happened, it was important for Fame to attend to his business. This had always been Harker's first rule: 'Keep the business going. The business must go on. Business first.' And so Fame crossed the frontier three times a week, every week of the year on business. Nobody outside Harker's gang knew what that business was. Even

Inspector Roland didn't know, although he wanted to know. And he had often tried to find out.

At the frontier post, the two customs officers Silver and Rank were busy. Earlier that morning, they had caught two men trying to smuggle a large amount of money across the border. Silver was writing his report about the smugglers, when the phone rang. He picked up the phone.

'Hello,' he said, 'Frontier. Silver speaking.'

'Inspector Roland here,' said the voice on the other end.

'Oh hello, Inspector,' said Silver, 'what can I do for you?'

'Keep your eyes open,' said the Inspector.

'Who for?' asked Silver.

'John Samuel Fame,' said the Inspector.

'Him again?' asked Silver.

'Yes,' said the Inspector. 'If he comes through, search his car very carefully.'

'What are you looking for?' asked Silver.

'The golden head of Chefren IV,' said the Inspector.

Silver whistled. 'Did Fame steal the head?' he asked.

'I don't know,' said the Inspector, 'perhaps. Anyway, keep your eyes open and search his car.'

'Of course, Inspector,' said Silver.

When Fame arrived at the frontier post about half an hour later, Silver and Rank were waiting for him.

'Good morning, Mr Fame,' said Rank. 'Going home?'

'Yes,' said Fame.

'Anything to declare?' asked Silver.

'Nothing,' said Fame.

'We'd like to have a look at your car,' said Rank.

'OK,' said Fame. And he smiled.

For the next hour, Rank and Silver searched Fame's car. They searched every part of the car twice and they even took up the carpet inside the car. But they found nothing – or, almost nothing.

'Have you had a crash?' asked Rank, pointing to the side of the car. There was a scratch above one of the wheels and someone had tried to paint over it.

'No,' said Fáme.

'Well, I don't remember this mark before,' said Rank.

'That scratch has always been there,' said Fame quickly.

Rank looked at Fame.

'All right, Mr Fame, you can go now. Everything's in order.'

'Thank you,' said Fame, 'I'm glad you're satisfied. See you tomorrow.'

'Are you coming back tomorrow?'

'Oh yes,' said Fame. 'Don't forget to search my car will you?'

And he drove off in a cloud of dust.

12

Ambush

Less than twenty-four hours later, Fame was back at the frontier. Once again his car was thoroughly searched, but once again Rank and Silver found nothing. They did not even find the scratch on Fame's car. Fame told them he had covered it with paint.

Fame left the frontier and drove towards Darna. He was in no hurry and he decided to stop for a coffee on the way. He knew a small café nearby.

Fame parked his car outside the café and went in. He ordered a coffee and sat down at a small table. A radio was playing and Fame sat there listening to the music.

The café was almost empty. The music on the radio stopped and a voice started to read the news. Fame had been out of the country for a day. He was interested in what had happened while he had been away.

Suddenly Fame sat up straight in his chair. The news on the radio was about Harker. The radio said that the police had just found the body of a man called Harker. Fame listened.

The news said that Harker's body had been found in a hut in the forest. The police thought that Harker had been murdered.

Fame finished his coffee quickly and left the café. So now Inspector Roland knew that Harker was dead. Don was still a hostage and now the Inspector would be looking for Fame. Fame decided to drive straight to Zara's house. So he hurried over to his car, got in and drove off towards Darna.

It was a beautiful day without a cloud in the sky. A slight wind moved the tops of the cypress trees along the straight white road. Fame began to forget his worries as he drove along under the cypress trees in the morning sun.

Fame didn't notice that there was a big blue car behind him. The blue car followed Fame for about a kilometre along the road. Then, just before the road began to climb into the hills, the blue car pulled out and accelerated past Fame and disappeared round the bend in front. Fame saw the blue car go past him, but he was only half-looking at the road. Above him, hanging in the sky, was a golden eagle. The eagle was hardly moving – its wings were spread and still. Fame slowed the car down and watched.

Suddenly the eagle dived towards the ground and disappeared behind the cypress trees. Then there was a scream of a small animal. The eagle had caught something – a hare perhaps, or a rat. Fame drove on.

The road was now climbing and turning through the hills. On the other side of the hills was the valley and the lake and the town of Darna. Near the highest point of the road, Fame saw a sign at the side of the road as he came round a corner. The sign had one word written on it: SLOW.

Fame slowed down. Someone must be working on the road,

The blue car followed Fame for about a kilometre
along the road.

mending it. Fame couldn't see anybody. The ground on the left side of the road climbed steeply to some trees; on the right it fell steeply into the valley. The road itself was narrower than anywhere else between the frontier and Darna.

Suddenly Fame heard a shot. There was a loud noise very close to him and then another. Someone was shooting at Fame's car. Fame tried to accelerate but the car was out of control. Fame tried to keep the car on the road. Bullets were hitting the car from all sides. Then there was a loud crack, and the windscreen broke into hundreds of pieces of glass. Fame could see nothing.

Fame put the brakes on as hard as he could and felt the car slide to the left, then to the right. Then the car turned a complete circle and stopped. Fame opened the door and ran. Then the shooting stopped.

Fame jumped over the edge of the road and rolled down the slope. Over and over he went until he reached the bottom. There were some bushes at the bottom of the slope and Fame pulled himself into the middle of them. He lay there, breathing heavily.

From above him, Fame heard a voice. It was Ezra's voice.

'All right, Fame, we've got you,' shouted Ezra. 'Come out of those bushes with your hands up.'

13

Another Journey

Fame got up, put his hands above his head, and came out of the bushes. He looked up. Ezra was looking down at him from the top of the slope. Next to Ezra was the bald-headed 'waiter' with the scar. There were also two other men. Fame and Zara had seen

Fame got up, put his hands above his head, and came out of the bushes.

these two men at the lakeside restaurant. One was tall and dark, the other was short and fat.

'Well, Fame,' said Ezra, 'nice to see you again.'

Fame said nothing.

'Go down and search him, boys,' said Ezra.

The tall dark man and the short fat man came down the slope towards Fame, while the bald-headed man pointed his gun at him. Fame kept his hands up while the two men searched his pockets.

'He hasn't got a gun, Boss,' said the tall dark man.

Fame recognised the voice; he had heard it somewhere. It was a high voice with an Italian accent.

'OK, Guido,' said Ezra, 'tie his hands.'

Guido took a piece of rope from his jacket pocket and tied Fame's hands behind his back. Then he and the fat man pushed Fame back up the slope towards the road.

Fame's car was right in the middle of the road. Broken glass from the windscreen lay all round the car, and one of the tyres was flat.

'Skull,' said Ezra to the bald man, 'you stay with his car. Change the wheel and knock out the rest of the glass. Then follow us.'

'Right, Boss,' said Skull.

Ezra turned to Fame.

'You're coming along with us,' he said. 'I've got a few things to ask you.'

Ezra turned and crossed the road. Guido and the fat man pushed Fame along behind him. Ezra walked a little way up the white road and then turned off down a lane. The branches of the trees hung low, shutting out the sun and making the lane dark. A big blue car was parked there. Fame recognised it. It was the car that had passed him earlier while he was watching the eagle.

'Put him in the back, Robert,' said Ezra to the short fat man. Robert pushed Fame into the back of the car. Then Robert sat on one side of Fame and Guido sat on the other side. Ezra got into the driver's seat and started the car. The car moved slowly forward, down the dark lane under the low hanging trees to the main road. Ezra turned left and drove towards Darna. Looking back, Fame saw that Skull had got his car to the side of the road and was changing the wheel.

They drove steadily towards Darna. Ezra didn't seem in a hurry. A few miles out of Darna, Ezra turned onto a small road. Fame knew this road. It also led into Darna. There was less chance of meeting any police cars on this road.

'Well, Fame,' Ezra said, after a few minutes, 'so you and I are enemies now.'

Fame said nothing.

'And Harker's dead,' said Ezra.

'So I heard on the radio,' said Fame.

Ezra looked at Fame in the driving mirror. Then he laughed.

'You heard about Harker's death on the radio, did you?' said Ezra.

'Yes,' said Fame. 'It's a bad business.'

'A very bad business,' said Ezra and laughed again.

Fame looked out of the window. They had reached Darna. Ezra turned the car into a narrow lane. The car bumped down the lane until it came to the last house. Ezra stopped the car.

'Take him out,' said Ezra to the two men, 'and take him inside.'

'Which room shall we put him in, Boss?' asked Robert, the fat man. This was the first time he had spoken, and Fame recognised the voice immediately. It was the voice he had heard in Harker's hut two days ago when he had discovered Harker's body. And that's where he had heard Guido's voice too. Now Fame remembered. Guido's voice had an Italian accent. Robert's voice was strong and deep.

'Put him in the cellar[15], Robert,' said Ezra. 'We don't want to make him too comfortable, do we?'

And Ezra laughed again.

14

Ezra's Place

The cellar was not a comfortable room. It was dark and small. Guido and Robert pushed Fame inside and locked the door. Fame was alone.

Hundreds of questions raced through Fame's mind, as he stood in that small dark cellar. What did Ezra want? What was Ezra going to do with him? What was Zara doing? Where was Don? What was Inspector Roland doing? Where was the golden head? What did that poem mean?

Fame wanted answers to all these questions.

The door opened and Guido came in.

'The Boss wants to see you,' he said. 'Upstairs.'

Guido pushed Fame out of the cellar and up some stone steps. At the top of the steps was a door. Guido knocked.

'Come in,' said a voice.

Guido opened the door and pushed Fame inside.

Fame found himself in a large comfortable room. Ezra was sitting behind a large desk with his back to a large window. The window opened out onto a balcony. On the floor of the room there was a Persian carpet and on the walls there were tall bookshelves full of books. On Ezra's desk there was a photograph. Fame saw that it was the same photograph Inspector Roland had showed him – the photograph taken at the museum reception.

'Sit down,' said Ezra, pointing to a chair in front of the desk. Fame sat down. Guido left the room.

'Cigar?' asked Ezra, opening a box of cigars and holding the box out to Fame.

'My hands are tied,' said Fame.

'Of course,' said Ezra, 'how stupid of me. Guido!' he shouted.

Guido, who had been waiting outside, came in.

46

'Untie his hands,' ordered Ezra.

Guido untied Fame's hands.

'You may go,' said Ezra to Guido.

Guido left the room.

'Cigar?' said Ezra again.

'Thank you,' said Fame and took one.

'Light?' asked Ezra, picking up a cigarette lighter from the desk and holding it out to Fame.

'Thank you,' said Fame, leaning forward with the cigar in his mouth.

Ezra lit Fame's cigar and sat back in his chair. There was a silence while both men smoked their cigars.

'Now,' said Ezra, after the silence, 'where is it?'

'Where's what?' asked Fame.

'You know,' said Ezra.

'I don't know,' said Fame.

'The head,' said Ezra.

'Oh the head,' said Fame.

'Yes,' said Ezra, 'the head. The golden head – the golden Egyptian head from the museum.'

'I don't know,' said Fame, 'I didn't steal it.'

'I know,' said Ezra, 'I know you didn't steal it. Harker stole it. But you know where it is, don't you?'

'No,' said Fame, 'I don't.'

Ezra took the cigar from his mouth and looked hard at Fame. Then he blew some smoke straight into Fame's face.

'Now, Fame,' he said, 'don't be stupid.'

'I'm not being stupid,' said Fame. 'I've no idea where the golden head is.'

Ezra put his left hand into his jacket pocket and pulled out a piece of paper. He pushed it across the desk to Fame.

'Have you seen that before?' asked Ezra.

'Yes,' said Fame. It was the poem Harker had written to Fame before he was killed.

47

'What does the poem mean?' asked Ezra.

'I've no idea,' said Fame.

'Read it aloud,' said Ezra.

So Fame read the poem aloud.

'Well, what does it mean?' asked Ezra again, when Fame had finished reading the poem.

'I don't know,' said Fame, 'I don't understand it.'

Ezra pressed a little button on his desk. The door behind Fame opened, and Guido and Robert came in.

'Tie him up again,' said Ezra, pointing to Fame.

Guido held Fame's hands, pulled them behind his back, and tied them with the same piece of rope. Robert knocked the cigar out of Fame's mouth. Ezra stood up and walked over to the window. He turned round and looked at Fame.

'I've been gentle with you so far,' said Ezra, 'but I'm getting a little impatient.'

'But I don't know any . . .' began Fame.

'You listen to me,' said Ezra. He was suddenly angry. 'Harker and I planned to steal the golden head together. *We* planned it. Harker wanted the golden head and I said I'd help him steal it. We planned the robbery together. I agreed to steal the head for Harker and take it to my room in the Imperial Hotel. But we argued. Harker and I had an argument. Harker got that head by himself – he got there before me.'

Ezra paused and wiped his hand over his mouth. At last he was telling Fame what had really happened. Fame stared at Ezra, waiting for Ezra to continue his story.

'When I discovered that Harker had stolen the head by himself,' continued Ezra, 'I was angry. Very angry. I went to Harker's hut in the forest and we argued. He wouldn't tell me where he had hidden the head of the Pharaoh.'

'So you killed him,' said Fame simply.

'Shut up,' said Ezra, 'I haven't finished yet. We killed Harker, but only after we had argued. I found this poem on Harker's desk, addressed to you. I asked him what it meant. He wouldn't tell me, but I knew it was important. I knew that there was a message hidden in the poem – about the head. Harker said that you would understand the poem. We argued. I lost my temper[16] and we killed him.'

'Who do you mean by "we"?' asked Fame.

'Guido, Robert and myself, of course,' said Ezra. 'We killed Harker, hung him up and then we left the hut quickly.'

'Why didn't you take the poem with you?' asked Fame.

Ezra looked at Robert, who was standing behind Fame.

'That fool Robert,' said Ezra, 'had the poem, but he must have dropped it as we were leaving. When we realised we had lost the poem, Robert and Guido hurried back to Harker's hut to look for the piece of paper with the poem on it. But instead of finding the poem, they found you. And you escaped with the poem.'

Ezra paused. He was now red in the face and breathing hard. Fame sat still in his chair, and Guido and Robert stood behind him. Outside the house, a car stopped. Fame heard the sound and realised that it was *his* car. Skull had returned.

Then Fame spoke.

'Now you have the poem,' said Fame. 'Why do you need me?'

'We need you,' said Ezra to Fame, 'because you understand the poem. I'll give you one more chance to tell me what the poem means. Where is the golden head? What does the poem say?'

Fame said nothing.

'What does the poem say?' asked Ezra again.

Fame still said nothing. Then Robert hit him.

15

Escape

Fame didn't remember afterwards how many times they hit him. He heard Ezra's voice asking the same question. But he said nothing. Ezra was very angry. He started shouting.

'Take him back to the cellar!' shouted Ezra. 'Leave him there for the night! Bring him back here in the morning! Take him away!'

So Fame was taken out and carried down the steps to the cellar. Guido and Robert threw him inside and locked the door.

For a long time, Fame lay on the cellar floor. There were several cuts on his head, and his back and shoulders ached. Fame fell asleep.

It was early evening when he finally woke. With difficulty, Fame stood up and walked towards the window. His face and shoulders still ached and there was dry blood on his shirt. But he felt quite calm and his head was very clear.

Fame thought about Ezra's story. He now knew for certain who had killed Harker and why. Ezra and his men had killed Harker, because Harker had stolen the golden head. Harker had stolen the head, without telling Ezra where he had hidden it. If Fame could understand the poem, he could learn where Harker had hidden the golden head.

Fame had to learn the meaning of the poem. But first he must untie his hands and escape from Ezra. Fame looked round the cellar.

In one corner, there were a few broken chairs and some wooden boxes. Near the boxes was an old iron bed. Fame walked across the cellar to the bed. He knelt on the stone floor with his back to the bed. Then he moved his arms against the side of the bed until the rope around his hands was right against the sharp

corner of the iron frame. Then Fame began to rub the rope against
the frame, slowly at first, then faster.

After about five minutes the rope began to break. Fame
rubbed harder and a moment later the rope broke. His hands
were free. Slowly Fame moved his arms round to the front. His
fingers were so stiff that he could hardly move them, and there
were deep white marks on his wrists where the ropes had been.

Fame picked up one of the broken chairs and carried it over to
the window. He put the chair against the wall under the window,
and stood rather unsteadily on it. Now he could see through the
window.

He was looking into a yard. In the middle of the yard was
his car. Someone had mended the windscreen. Skull, the bald-
headed man, was standing beside the car.

It was now nearly dark. The sun had gone and Fame could
hear the evening noises beginning – insects, children playing, and

the noise of plates as someone prepared supper. Fame decided to wait until it was completely dark.

He looked at the window. It was small but it was the only way out of the cellar. The window had a wooden frame and wire had been nailed to the frame. Fame got down from the chair and felt on the floor for a tool to pull off the wire. In the darkness his hands felt something cold and hard. It was a large bent nail.

Fame got back on the chair and looked out again. Skull had disappeared. Very gently, Fame pushed the nail under the wire and began to pull the wire away from the frame. It was slow work but after about quarter of an hour Fame had pulled one corner of the wire back from the frame. Fame worked on.

It was not completely dark. There was one dim light in the yard. Someone came out of a door and crossed the yard. Fame saw his face as he passed under the light. It was Ezra.

It took Fame about an hour to pull off the wire. Once he heard footsteps coming up to the cellar door, but nobody came in. Then Fame could hear laughter from one of the rooms across the yard. Ezra and his men must be having supper.

When Fame had removed the wire, he put his head through the window and looked out. There was no one in the yard. He pulled his head back in and waited a moment. All was quiet. He started to go through the window but it wasn't easy. The window was small. But Fame pushed and turned his body until at last he was through the window.

As soon as he was in the yard, Fame went to his car. He looked inside. To his surprise, Skull had left the keys in the car. Fame was about to get in, when a door opened and two men came into the yard. Fame dropped down and lay flat on the ground beside the car.

'Well now,' said a voice, 'I think it's time we asked our friend Fame some more questions.' It was Ezra's voice.

'Shall I go and get him, Boss?' It was Guido's voice.

'OK,' said Ezra. 'Bring him up to my room.'

'Right, Boss,' said Guido.

Both men moved away.

Fame did not wait. He jumped into the car, turned the key to start the engine and accelerated out of the yard. There were shouts behind him. Looking in the mirror, Fame saw that both Ezra and Guido, the Italian, were running. Fame accelerated down the narrow street.

He was in a poor part of town, where all the streets were narrow and badly lit. There was no traffic and there were few people in the streets.

Fame looked in the mirror again and saw that the big blue car was following him. Ezra was driving the blue car and Guido was sitting beside him. Fame drove fast but he didn't know the streets. Ezra did. Slowly the blue car came nearer to him. Fame turned his car into another sloping narrow street. Both cars were going very fast.

Suddenly Fame saw that there was a wall ahead. The street had no exit. There was no way out.

Fame put on the brakes to stop the car. The tyres screamed on the dry road and the car moved wildly from left to right and then came to a stop. Fame pulled the keys out of the car and jumped out. To his left, there was an opening in the wall. Beyond it was another street. Fame ran through the opening.

Fame ran through the opening.

16

Trapped!

In front of Fame was a high wall; behind him were Ezra and
Guido. Fame could hear Ezra and Guido shouting behind
him. They were following him through the opening and down
the narrow street.

Fame turned right suddenly and ran back down a very small
path. There were no lights at all in the path and once he fell over
a broken box lying against the wall.

At the end of the path there were some steps which dropped
into the darkness. As Fame ran down the steps, he fell over onto
the stone pavement at the bottom. By now, Ezra and Guido had
reached the top of the steps. Fame couldn't see them, but he could
hear them shouting to each other.

Fame got up and ran on. He couldn't see anything in front of
him and there was a sharp pain in his left leg, but he had to keep
going. After about another ten metres, he suddenly saw the black
shape of a wall in front of him. He saw the wall too late and ran
straight into it.

Fame was trapped. There was no way that he could escape. On
one side of him was a high wall; on the other side were Ezra and
Guido. The wall was too high to climb, and Fame could find no
door or window that led through it. He turned to face Ezra and
Guido. He could hear them both breathing, only a few metres away.

'Fame! Where are you?' called Ezra.

'We're coming to get you,' said Guido. 'You can't escape
now.'

So far Ezra and Guido hadn't seen Fame. They were both
coming forward very slowly towards the wall. Fame moved a
little to his left. As he did so, he felt a piece of metal in the
wall. It was a door handle. Very gently Fame turned the handle

and silently opened the door. He opened the door wide enough to slip through. Then, quick as a cat, he closed the door behind him and felt to see if there was a key. There was a large key and Fame turned it to lock the door. He heard an angry shout from Ezra, on the other side of the wall. Fame had escaped.

Fame seemed to be in a garden. There was a smell of lemons and he could just see the shape of a large bush to the left of the door. In the distance there was a light and Fame began to move slowly towards it. He was walking on soft earth and the smell of lemons was very strong. The light was coming from the window of a house, and Fame could see the dark shape of the building against the sky. He walked carefully on until he had reached the side of the house just below the window.

There was a pile of boxes directly under the window. Fame reached up to pull himself on top of the pile so that he could look through the window. As he was pulling himself up, Fame knocked one of the boxes with his knee. The whole pile of boxes fell to the ground and Fame fell with them.

Almost immediately Fame heard voices coming towards him. Suddenly someone shone a torch on Fame as he lay among the broken boxes. Then Fame heard a voice that he knew very well.

'Well, Mr Fame,' said the voice. 'What a surprise to see you. Welcome to police headquarters[17].'

Fame looked up from the pile of boxes on the ground. Looking down at him was Inspector Roland.

17

Plans

Fame picked himself up.

'Hello, Inspector,' he said, 'I've come to see you.'

'So I see,' said Inspector Roland. 'Are you staying?'

'If you want me to,' said Fame.

Inspector Roland smiled.

'You're staying,' said the Inspector.

And two policemen took Fame by the arms and led him into the police headquarters.

Fame was led into a large room with a lot of maps on one wall and a very large painting of the president on the opposite wall. In the middle of the room was a long table with eight chairs round it.

'Sit down, Fame,' said Inspector Roland pointing to one of the chairs.

Fame sat down. So did the others. Apart from Inspector Roland there were three other people in the room – two policemen and a woman holding a notebook.

'Well,' said Inspector Roland cheerfully, looking at Fame. 'And where have you been?'

'Here and there,' said Fame.

'Doing what?' asked the Inspector.

'Thinking,' said Fame.

'Did you find Harker?' asked the Inspector.

'Harker's dead,' said Fame.

'I know,' said Inspector Roland. 'Did you kill him?'

'No,' said Fame, 'but I know who did. Ezra. Ezra and his men killed Harker.'

There was a silence.

'Do you want to tell us what happened?' said the Inspector.

'All right,' said Fame.

Fame began to tell the Inspector what had happened. He told Inspector Roland about the hut in the forest, the argument between Harker and Ezra, and about Harker's plan to steal the golden head. He told the Inspector how Harker had stolen the head and how Ezra, Guido and Robert had killed him.

Inspector Roland listened to Fame's story. Then Fame told the Inspector how Ezra and his men had captured him and asked him many questions. Fame explained how he had escaped from Ezra.

'I see,' said Inspector Roland when Fame had finished. 'Very interesting, but there's something else I'd like to know – something you haven't told me.'

'What's that?' asked Fame.

'Where the head is. The golden head. Where is the golden head of the Pharaoh, stolen from the museum by Harker?'

'I don't know where it is,' said Fame.

Inspector Roland leant forward.

'Look, Fame,' he said, 'you're an intelligent man. I'm an intelligent man. Let's not play games.'

'What do you mean?' said Fame.

'Listen,' said the Inspector, 'I know you worked for Harker and I know Ezra worked for Harker. Harker had a gang, didn't he?'

'Yes,' said Fame.

'Now I've been trying to catch Harker and his gang for a long time. You and he and the gang have been smuggling for years, haven't you?'

'Well . . .' said Fame.

'Yes you have,' said the Inspector. 'I know you have. But I don't know *what* you've been smuggling. But if you don't help me, you and your friends are going to go to prison.'

'What for?' asked Fame.

'For stealing the golden head of the Pharaoh Chefren IV.'

'But . . .' began Fame. 'You could never prove that we stole the head. You know we didn't steal it. I've told you that Harker stole the head.'

'I think I could prove that you stole the head,' said Inspector Roland. 'There's a lot of evidence[18] against you.'

Fame was silent. It was true. There *was* a lot of evidence against him. He was Harker's most important man. He had the mysterious poem. He had had an appointment with Harker the night Harker was killed . . .

Inspector Roland took a piece of paper off the desk and showed it to Fame. Fame immediately recognised what was written on the paper. It was Harker's poem.

'Where did you get this?' asked Fame.

'From your friend,' said Inspector Roland.

'Which friend?' asked Fame.

'Your girlfriend,' said the Inspector.

'Zara?' asked Fame, amazed.

'Zara,' said the Inspector. As he spoke, the Inspector picked up a small silver bell from the table and rang it. Almost immediately the door opened and Zara and Don came in, followed by a policeman.

18

The Poem

'Zara!' said Fame.
'Hello, Fame,' said Zara.
'Hello, Fame,' said Don.
'Hello, Don,' said Fame.

'Well,' said Inspector Roland, 'now you've all met, I'll tell you what I'm going to do. I'm going to leave you in this room with two of my men to guard you, and . . .' he held up Harker's poem, 'with this piece of paper. Now, I'll give you until morning to tell me the meaning of this poem. If you work it out and tell me where the golden head is hidden, you'll be free. If you don't work it out, you'll be charged with stealing the golden head of the Pharaoh Chefren IV.'

'But we didn't steal it,' said Zara.

'There's a lot of evidence against you,' said Inspector Roland, smiling. Then he left the room while the two policemen stayed behind.

Zara, Fame and Don looked at each other.

'Well,' said Zara, 'let's have a look at the poem.'

Fame picked up the piece of paper.

Fame read it out:

> *Great men*
> *Do not walk easy roads.*
> *Tall men*
> *Strain under heavy loads.*
> *They bend beneath the weight,*
> *Get tired beneath the load.*
> *They go in pain and hate.*
> *They wander down that road,*
> *But then against the wall they stand*
> *And near one rock, they rest their hand.*

When Fame had read the poem he looked at Don and Zara.

'Well?' he asked.

'It's nonsense,' said Don. 'It doesn't mean anything.'

'It's a poem,' said Zara. 'It means a lot.'

'It's more than a poem,' said Fame. 'There's a message in it.'

'What message?' asked Don.

'I don't know,' said Fame. 'Let's try and find out.'

'How?' asked Zara.

'Well,' said Fame. 'Let's look at the letters at the beginning of each line.'

Fame took another piece of paper from his pocket and wrote down the letters at the beginning of each line.

GDTSTGTTBA

'What does that spell?' asked Don.

'Nothing,' said Zara.

'Let's try the letters the other way round,' said Fame.

'How do you mean?' said Don.

'Like this,' said Fame, and he wrote the letters down backwards:

ABTTGTSTDG

'What does that spell?' asked Don.

'Nothing,' said Zara.

'OK,' said Fame, 'let's try something else. Let's take the first letter of the first line, and the last letter of the second line . . . and so on . . .'

'How do you mean?' asked Don.

'Like this,' said Fame, and he wrote down:

GSTSTDTDBD

'What does that spell?' asked Don.

'Nothing,' said Zara.

'Try the letters the other way round,' said Fame.

And this time Don wrote them down:

DBDTDTSTSG

'It still doesn't spell anything,' said Zara.

'I know,' said Fame.

'It's nonsense,' said Don.

Fame shook his head. The two policemen were watching them from the other end of the room.

'I've got an idea,' said Zara suddenly.

'What is it?' asked Fame.

'Take the first letter of the first line and the second letter of the second line, and so on.'

'How do you mean?' asked Don.

'Like this,' said Zara. 'Fame, what's the first letter of the first line?'

'G,' said Fame.

'And the second letter of the second line?' asked Zara.

'O,' said Fame.

'And the third letter of the third line?'

'L.'

'And the fourth letter of the fourth line?'

'A.'

'And the fifth letter of the fifth line?'

'B.'

'And the sixth letter of the sixth line?'

'R.'

'And the seventh letter of the seventh line?'

'I.'

'And the eighth letter of the eighth line?'

'D,' said Fame.

'And the ninth letter of the ninth line?'

'G.'

'And the tenth letter of the tenth line?'

'E,' said Fame.

'What does that spell?' asked Don. He was laughing.

'Let's see,' said Fame.

GOLABRIDGE

Fame looked at Zara. She was looking at Fame. She was going to shout but Fame stopped Zara from shouting. They had discovered the message hidden in the poem, but Fame didn't want the policemen to know. Fame made a sign. 'Oh dear, it doesn't spell anything,' he said loudly. He looked at the two policemen. They weren't even looking.

'Gola Bridge,' whispered Zara. 'So that's the message in the poem.'

'Gola Bridge,' whispered Don, 'of course, the bridge over the River Gola, not far from my hide-out.'

'So that's where the head's hidden,' whispered Fame.

Fame looked at the policemen again. One of them was looking out of the window and the other was yawning. Fame looked at Zara. Zara nodded. She understood what Fame wanted to do next. She coughed. The two policemen looked at her.

'Excuse me,' said Zara.

'What do you want?' asked one of the policemen.

'I'd like a drink of water,' said Zara. 'I'm thirsty.'

'All right,' said the policeman. 'I'll get you a drink of water.' And he went out of the room to get a glass of water for Zara. There was now only one policeman in the room.

'Excuse me,' said Fame to the policeman.

'What do you want?' said the policeman.

'We want some help,' said Fame.

'What with?' asked the policeman.

'This poem,' said Fame.

'What's the difficulty?' asked the policeman, coming over to Fame.

'Is this letter a G or a Y?' asked Fame.

The policeman bent over the bit of paper. Very quickly, Don moved behind the policeman and hit him hard on the back of the head with his open hand. The policeman fell onto the floor.

'Quick,' said Don, 'the other policeman will be back soon.'

Don stood behind the door and Fame and Zara stood in front of the fallen policeman. The door opened and the other policeman came in, carrying a glass of water.

'I've brought you your . . .' said the policeman. But he didn't finish the sentence. Don held him from behind and hit him. The glass dropped onto the carpet. Don caught the policeman as he fell.

63

'Into the garden,' said Fame to Don and Zara.

They opened the door into the garden and went out. Behind them on the table lay the piece of paper with 'GOLABRIDGE' written on it.

19

The Search

Fame led Zara and Don back through the garden to the door in the wall and out into the street. They walked back quietly to where Fame had left his car. The moon had come up, lighting the paths and the streets. There was no sign of Ezra or Guido. There was no sign of their car either. But Fame's car was still there.

Zara, Don and Fame got into the car quickly. Fame backed the car up the narrow street, turned, and drove out of Darna. Zara and Don didn't ask where they were going. They knew where they were going. The moon was shining brightly and it was a warm night. Fame drove fast through the empty streets and into the country. They passed the turn to Don's hide-out and then Fame turned the car off the main road and down a lane. After about two kilometres, they heard the sound of running water. It was the sound of the Gola river running down to Lake Darna.

Fame stopped the car before the bridge and the three of them looked out. They could see the huge black shape of the Gola Bridge in front of them. Above them on one side of the road, was a steep hill. On the other side, was a steep drop down to the river.

'We're here,' said Fame.

They looked at the bridge.

'Where do we begin the search?' asked Zara, 'The bridge is so big.'

They could see the huge black shape of the Gola Bridge in front of them.

'I don't think the head is hidden on the bridge at all,' said Fame.

'Where is it hidden then?' asked Don.

'Look at the poem again,' said Fame.

He took the poem out of his pocket. Then he got a torch from the car and switched it on. They all looked at the poem.

'Right,' said Fame, 'listen. Zara discovered the most important thing: the words "Gola Bridge". But the bridge is very big and there's nowhere very safe to hide the head. I think the head is somewhere very near the bridge. Now there are some clues in the poem. Listen:

"Great men

Do *not* walk *easy roads*."'

'What does that mean?' asked Don.

'You know the old quarry[19] up there on the hillside, don't you?' asked Fame.

'Of course I do,' replied Don. 'My father used to work in the quarry.'

'Well,' said Fame, 'the path to the quarry is rough and difficult, isn't it?'

'Yes, it is,' Don agreed.

'And the workers who went up and down to the quarry carried heavy loads, didn't they?' asked Fame. 'That's in the fourth line of the poem:

"Strain under *heavy loads*"'

'Then the Pharaoh's head must be hidden in the quarry,' said Zara.

'Yes, it must be hidden very near the quarry,' replied Fame. 'But listen to the last two lines of the poem. There are two more clues in the poem:

"But then *against the wall* they stand

And *near one rock*, they rest their hand."'

Fame looked up at the others. They were all silent for a moment and then Don shouted out.

'I know what the last two lines of the poem mean,' he shouted. 'The wall is the wall of the quarry. When you get to the quarry, you come to the quarry wall, don't you?'

'Yes, you do,' said Zara.

'And next to the quarry wall there is a large rock,' said Don. 'In the rock there is a small cave.'

Don looked at Zara and then at Fame. They all smiled. So the Pharaoh's head was hidden in the rock, next to the quarry wall.

They got out of the car and walked up the narrow path to the quarry. The moon threw the shadows of the bushes across the path. It was very quiet. When they got to the quarry they walked to the quarry wall. They could see the shape of a large rock by the wall.

'Come on,' said Fame and began to climb up the side of the rock. Don and Zara followed him. The rock was quite easy to climb. Near the top of the rock was a small cave. Fame flashed the torch in the darkness. Something shone. Fame ran forward and picked up something. It was the golden head of the Pharaoh.

'What are you going to do with it?' asked Don.

'Send it to Inspector Roland, of course,' said Fame. 'He wants the head. We don't want it. We just want to continue with our usual business. Yes, we'll send the head to Inspector Roland.'

'Oh no, you won't,' said a voice.

It was Ezra, standing just below the rock with a gun in his

hand. With him were Guido the Italian, fat Robert, and Skull. They all had guns.

20

Shot Dead

'Come down,' said Ezra.

Fame, Zara and Don came down, carrying the head.

'I'll take that,' said Ezra, pointing to the golden head. Fame gave the head to Ezra, and Ezra smiled.

'At last,' said Ezra.

'Very clever,' said Fame.

'Yes, it was quite clever, wasn't it?' said Ezra. 'We simply followed you here.'

'How?' asked Fame.

'I knew you'd come back to your car,' said Ezra. 'We simply waited round the corner until you did come back. Then we drove behind you, parked the car a little way from the bridge and walked. We could hear you up by the quarry, so we followed you up the quarry path.'

'And now, here you are,' said Fame.

'Exactly,' said Ezra.

'What are you going to do with us?' asked Fame.

'Well,' said Ezra, 'we don't really need you any more, so I think we'll send you on a journey.'

'A journey?' asked Don.

'Yes,' said Ezra. 'Come with us.'

He pointed with his gun to the path from the quarry down to the road.

'That way,' he said.

So Fame, Don, and Zara walked back down the path followed by Ezra and his men with their guns. When they reached the road,

Fame's car was still parked on the road facing the bridge.

Ezra whispered something to Guido. Guido got into Fame's car and turned it across the road. Fame's car now faced the edge of the slope that dropped steeply down to the river.

'Now,' said Ezra, 'you three are all going to get into your car, and then you, Fame, are going to drive it over the slope and into the river. I hope you can swim, because if not, there'll be a little accident.'

Ezra smiled; the Italian smiled; Robert smiled; even Skull smiled. Fame, Zara, and Don, didn't smile.

'Come on,' said Ezra, 'get into the car.'

Fame opened the door slowly.

'Why don't you let us go?' he asked Ezra.

'Because I don't like you,' said Ezra. 'Get in!'

Fame got into his car and so did Zara and Don. In front of them was the steep drop down to the river.

'Now start the car,' said Ezra.

Fame started the car. Below them lay the river. The moon was reflected in the river.

'Goodbye,' said Ezra, waving at them and smiling. 'Have a safe . . .'

But Ezra never finished his sentence. Suddenly, there was the sound of a gun up the lane. Ezra stood with his mouth open, and one arm in the air. Then he turned slowly and fell.

Fame looked down the lane and saw three men running towards the car. Fame recognised the man who was carrying the gun. It was Inspector Roland.

Fame did not wait. He turned his car back onto the road and accelerated towards the bridge. Inspector Roland saw the car race across the Gola Bridge and disappear.

The Inspector bent down beside the body of Ezra and quietly picked up the golden head of the Pharaoh Chefren IV. His men were taking away Guido, Robert and Skull.

'Well,' said the Inspector to the Pharaoh, 'welcome back.'

21

A Long Time Later

It was five years later. Chief Inspector Roland was abroad, on holiday. He was staying in a small fishing town beside the sea.

One evening, he was sitting at a café table on the pavement, drinking a cup of coffee and smoking a cigarette.

He leant back and blew a puff of cigarette smoke into the sky. It was a beautiful warm night with a full moon. The sky was full of of stars. He felt very happy. Inspector Roland shut his eyes . . .

'Inspector Roland!' said a voice.

The Inspector opened his eyes. Someone was calling him. Standing on the other side of the café table was John Samuel Fame. There was a woman beside him. It was Zara. Inspector Roland stood up.

'Fame,' he said, 'and Zara.'

'Hello, Inspector,' said Zara.

'Sit down,' said Inspector Roland. 'Please sit down.'

So Fame and Zara sat down, and Inspector Roland ordered two more coffees, and they talked. They talked for a long time – into the early morning – like old friends. Inspector Roland told them about the golden head which was now safe in the Darna museum, and about Guido and Robert and Skull, just out of prison and now leading honest lives. The Inspector told them about Harker and Ezra, buried side by side in the hill cemetery above Darna. Fame and Zara told the Inspector about their marriage, about their two children, about their house and garden and their happiness together.

It was one o'clock in the morning when Fame looked at his watch.

'We must go,' he said to Zara. 'I'm tired.' They both stood up.

'Goodbye, Inspector,' said Fame, shaking hands, 'it's been wonderful meeting you again.'

'I've enjoyed it,' said the Inspector smiling. 'Goodbye, Zara.'

'Goodbye, Inspector,' said Zara. And she smiled.

They turned and started to walk down the street. Inspector Roland watched them. Then he remembered.

'Fame!' he shouted.

Fame stopped and turned. 'Yes?' he said.

'One question,' said the Inspector. 'What were you smuggling all those years, when you worked for Harker?'

There was a silence. Fame looked at Zara. She nodded. Fame turned to the Inspector again.

'Cars,' he said.

The Inspector stood with his mouth open.

'Cars!' he said, amazed.

'Yes,' said Fame, 'cars.'

'But,' said the Inspector, 'you only had one car.'

'That's what you thought,' said Fame, smiling.

'You mean that every time you crossed the frontier you were driving a different car?' asked the Inspector.

'That's right,' said Fame. 'The number plate was always the same, and the colour and type of car was always the same, but it was a different car each time.'

'But how . . .?' said the Inspector. 'Why . . .?'

He was speechless.

'Very simple,' said Fame. 'On my side of the frontier, we made cars; on your side of the frontier you needed cars. On my side of the frontier, cars were cheap; on your side of the frontier, cars were expensive. So, I drove a new car from my country into your country. I told the customs it was my car. When I got to Don's hide-out, Don took the new car. Then he gave me a secondhand[20] car – same colour, same type as the new car – and I drove back to my country. Each time I came into your country, I was in a new car but the car's number was the same. So we made a lot of money; we paid no tax and we sold the new cars for a good price. And nobody guessed. You all looked inside the car; you didn't look at the car itself . . .'

There was a silence.

'Well,' said the Inspector, 'I don't know what to say.'

'Say nothing,' said Fame. 'It was all a long time ago.'

And turning, Fame took Zara by the hand and walked away.

Points for Understanding

1

1 Where was Harker?
2 Why did Ezra come to Harker's hut?
3 Who was Harker's poem addressed to?

2

1 How often did Fame cross the frontier?
2 Did Inspector Roland believe Fame was a businessman?
3 Why did the Inspector phone Rank and Silver?
4 What did Rank and Silver find in Fame's car?

3

1 Where did Fame go after crossing the frontier?
2 What had happened to Harker?

4

1 Why did Fame think the poem important and unusual?
2 Had the two men been to Harker's hut recently?
3 What were the two men looking for?
4 What sort of voices did the two men have?

5

1 Why had Harker written a poem with a message in it?
2 Did Fame understand the message in Harker's poem?
3 Who did Fame phone from the hotel in Darna?
4 What had been stolen from the museum?

6

1 Why had Ezra left Harker's gang the week before?
2 Who was now Fame's boss?
3 What did the second waiter look like?
4 What do you think happened to Zara?

7

1 What had the bald-headed man taken from Zara?
2 Who was Don?
3 Who were the men dressed in black?

8

1 Why did Inspector Roland and his policemen go to Don's shed?
2 What did they find in the cars in Don's shed?

9

1 What was the Inspector looking for?
2 Who did Fame recognise in the photograph?
3 What was written on the back of the photograph and who wrote it?
4 Did the Inspector know that Harker was dead?
5 What arrangement did Fame suggest to Inspector Roland?
6 Why did the Inspector agree to Fame's suggested arrangement?

10

1 Who did Zara and Fame recognise at the restaurant?
2 Where had they seen this man before?
3 What did the other two men look like?
4 What did 'C 304' mean?
5 Who was staying in rooms 303 and 304 of the Imperial Hotel?

11

1 What had been the first rule of Harker's gang?
2 Did Inspector Roland know what the business of the gang was?
3 Did Rank notice anything different about Fame's car at the frontier?

12

1 What had Inspector Roland learnt about Harker?
2 Who attacked Fame on the road to Darna?

13

1 Who did Skull, Guido and Robert work for?
2 What did Skull look like?
3 Where had Fame and Zara seen Skull before?
4 What did Robert and Guido look like?
5 Where had Fame heard the voices of Robert and Guido before?
6 What did Ezra's men do with Fame?

14

1 Who had stolen the golden head?
2 Who had killed Harker?
3 Why had two of the murderers returned to Harker's hut after the murder?
4 Why was the poem so important?
5 Why did the murderers need Fame?

15

1 How did Fame untie his hands?
2 How did Fame get out of the cellar?

16

1 Who chased Fame?
2 What building did Fame escape into?
3 Who was shining the torch at Fame's face?

17

1 Did Fame tell the Inspector who killed Harker?
2 Fame said he didn't know where Harker had hidden the golden head. Was he telling the truth?
3 Did the Inspector know that Fame was a member of Harker's gang?
4 Did Inspector Roland know what the gang was smuggling?
5 What was on the piece of paper which the Inspector gave to Fame?
6 What had happened to Zara?

18

1 Why did Inspector Roland give Fame, Zara and Don the poem?
2 Where were Fame, Zara and Don going when they left the police headquarters?
3 Why were they going there?

19

1 Where did Don, Zara and Fame find the golden head?
2 What were they going to do with the head?
3 Who stopped them?

20

1 What happened to Don, Zara and Fame?
2 What happened to Ezra?
3 Who had the head in the end?

21

1 Where was the golden head five years later?
2 What had Fame and the gang been smuggling all those years?

Glossary

1 **gang** (page 5)
a group of people, like smugglers, who work together and do jobs that are not honest.

2 **sweat** (page 8)
when you are very hot or afraid, little drops of water come out of your body. This is to sweat.

3 **boot** – *of a car* (page 12)
the part of a car, usually at the back, where you put cases, boxes, etc.

4 **appointment** (page 13)
an agreement to meet someone at a certain time in a certain place.

5 **accelerate** (page 13)
to make a car go faster.

6 **roar forward/away** (page 13)
to drive quickly and make a very loud noise at the same time.

7 **shadow** (page 14)
when you stand in front of a strong light, the dark shape on the ground behind you is your shadow.

8 **boss** (page 19)
the leader of the gang.

9 **hide-out** (page 20)
a place where you can get away from other people and do things secretly.

10 **job** (page 21)
this usually means the work that a person does in return for money e.g. a customs officer. But here, a job means a particular piece of work that has been carefully planned.

11 **horn** (page 24)
part of a car which is used to make a warning noise.

12 **suspiciously** (page 28)
to look carefully at someone because you think they have done something wrong.

13 **reception** (page 30)
a party given for someone or something important.

14 **hostage** (page 32)
someone who is captured in order to force someone else to do something. If Fame or Zara try to run away, Don will be punished – he is the hostage.

15 *cellar* (page 45)
a dark room at the bottom of a house.
16 *lose one's temper* (page 49)
to become so angry that you shout loudly and perhaps try to hit someone.
17 *police headquarters* (page 56)
the building in a town in which the police have their most important offices.
18 *evidence* (page 59)
evidence against a person is anything which shows that a person has done something wrong.
19 *quarry* (page 66)
a place where men dig large stones out of the ground. The stones are used for making roads, bridges, buildings, etc.
20 *secondhand* (page 72)
if you buy a car that is not completely new, it is a secondhand car. You are not the first person to own the car.

Shane *by Jack Schaefer*
Old Mali and the Boy *by D. R. Sherman*
Bristol Murder *by Philip Prowse*
Tales of Goha *by Leslie Caplan*
The Smuggler *by Piers Plowright*
The Pearl *by John Steinbeck*
Things Fall Apart *by Chinua Achebe*
The Woman Who Disappeared *by Philip Prowse*
The Moon is Down *by John Steinbeck*
A Town Like Alice *by Nevil Shute*
The Queen of Death *by John Milne*
Walkabout *by James Vance Marshall*
Meet Me in Istanbul *by Richard Chisholm*
The Great Gatsby *by F. Scott Fitzgerald*
The Space Invaders *by Geoffrey Matthews*
My Cousin Rachel *by Daphne du Maurier*
I'm the King of the Castle *by Susan Hill*
Dracula *by Bram Stoker*
The Sign of Four *by Sir Arthur Conan Doyle*
The Speckled Band and Other Stories *by Sir Arthur Conan Doyle*
The Eye of the Tiger *by Wilbur Smith*
The Queen of Spades and Other Stories *by Aleksandr Pushkin*
The Diamond Hunters *by Wilbur Smith*
When Rain Clouds Gather *by Bessie Head*
Banker *by Dick Francis*
No Longer at Ease *by Chinua Achebe*
The Franchise Affair *by Josephine Tey*
The Case of the Lonely Lady *by John Milne*

For further information on the full selection of
Readers at all five levels in the series, please refer
to the Heinemann Guided Readers catalogue.

Heinemann English Language Teaching
A division of Reed Educational and Professional Publishing Limited
Halley Court, Jordan Hill, Oxford OX2 8EJ

OXFORD   MADRID   FLORENCE   ATHENS   PRAGUE
SÃO PAULO   MEXICO CITY   CHICAGO   PORTSMOUTH (NH)
TOKYO   SINGAPORE   KUALA LUMPUR   MELBOURNE
AUCKLAND   JOHANNESBURG   IBADAN   GABORONE

ISBN 0 435 27242 X

A recorded version of this story is available on cassette.
ISBN 0 435 27281 0

Illustrated by Clifford Bayly
Typography by Adrian Hodgkins
Cover by Ben Fowler and Threefold Design
Typeset in 11/12.5 pt Goudy
by Joshua Associates Ltd, Oxford
Printed and bound in Malta by Interprint Limited

96   97   10   9   8   7